The Gia

By Josie Stewart and Lynn Salem
Illustrations by Jason Hollback

Once there was a giant who wanted a job.
He saw a sign in the bakery.

In went the giant and asked for a job.
"You can bake bread," said the baker.

So the giant baked giant-sized loaves of bread.
"Oh my, that's not right," said the giant.
"I'll try something else."

He walked to the gas station.
In went the giant and asked for a job.
"You can fix cars," said the man.

So the giant fixed the cars.
He put big, huge tires
and very loud horns on them.

"Oh my, that's not right," said the giant.
"I'll try something else."

He walked down the street.
He asked the TV reporter for a job.
"You can report the news," she said.

So the giant shouted the news to everyone.
"Oh my, that's not right."
Off went the giant to try something else.

He walked to the space station.

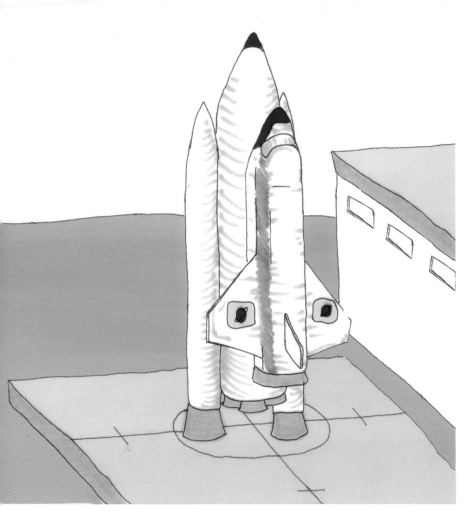

10-9-8-7-6-5-4-3-2-1
But, no blast off!
"I can help," said the giant.

The giant lifted the space shuttle
into the air and off it went.
Now the giant has a job.